POETRY AND LIFE

BOOK FOUR

Compiled by
NORA GRISENTHWAITE, M.A. Oxon
Principal Lecturer in English
Cheshire College of Education, Crewe

SCHOFIELD & SIMS LIMITED
HUDDERSFIELD

0 7217 0098 5

First edition April 1961
Second impression September 1961
Third impression June 1962
Fourth impression June 1964
Fifth impression June 1966
Sixth impression September 1967
Seventh impression August 1968
Eighth impression September 1969
Ninth impression April 1971
Tenth impression June 1972
Eleventh impression December 1973
Twelfth impression November 1974
Thirteenth impression June 1976

PRINTED IN ENGLAND BY
WILLMER BROTHERS LIMITED
BIRKENHEAD

Foreword

The poems in these anthologies have been chosen because they are worth reading and because children like them.

Book I is for children aged seven and eight.
Book II   ,,   eight and nine.
Book III   ,,   nine and ten.
Book IV   ,,   ten and eleven.

Acknowledgements

We are indebted to the following authors, executors and publishers for permission to include in this book the poems indicated.

Smells from 'Chimney Smoke' by Christopher Morley, to Methuen and Co. Ltd.

Marching Song from 'The Three Royal Monkeys', *The Snowflake, Ice, Rain, The Listeners* and *Tartary* by Walter de La Mare, to the Literary Trustees of Walter de la Mare and to the Society of Authors.

Dunkirk 1940 from 'Tonypandy' by Idris Davies, to Faber & Faber Ltd.

The Canary by Ogden Nash, to J. M. Dent & Sons Ltd.

The Ship by Richard Church, to J. M. Dent & Sons Ltd. and Laurence Pollinger Ltd.

The Hen and the Carp from 'The Weaver Birds' by Ian Serraillier, to the author.

Song of the Little Hunter from 'The Second Jungle Book' by Rudyard Kipling, to Mrs George Bambridge and Macmillan & Co. Ltd.

On a Night of Snow from 'Night and the Cat' by Elizabeth Coatsworth, to the Macmillan Co. New York.

Michael's Song by Wilfred Gibson to Macmillan & Co. Ltd.

The Way through the Woods from 'Rewards and Fairies' and *Puck's Song* from 'Puck of Pook's Hill' by Rudyard Kipling, to Mrs George Bambridge, Macmillan & Co. Ltd. and A. P. Watt & Son.

Snow in the Suburbs from Collected Poems of Thomas Hardy, to the Trustees of the Hardy Estate and Macmillan & Co. Ltd.

The Tarry Buccaneer and *Trade Winds* from Collected Poems of John Masefield, to The Society of Authors and to the Macmillan Co. New York.

The Fog from Collected Poems of W. H. Davies, to Mrs H. M. Davies and Jonathan Cape Ltd.

The Eagle from Collected Poems of Andrew Young, to Rupert Hart-Davies Ltd.

ACKNOWLEDGEMENTS

Winter, the Huntsman from 'Selected Poems Old and New' by
   Osbert Sitwell, and *Matilda* from 'Cautionary Tales for
   Children' by Hilaire Belloc, to Gerald Duckworth & Co. Ltd.
English from 'The Children's Bells' by Eleanor Farjeon, *Uriconium*
   from 'The Blackbird in the Lilac' by James Reeves and *Fish in
   Pacific Waters* from 'A Ballad of Kon Tiki' by Ian Serraillier,
   to The Oxford University Press.
Wind and Silver by Amy Lowell, from 'Modern American Poetry',
   to Houghton, Mifflin Co.
Space Travellers by James Nimmo, from 'Oxford Books of Verse
   for Juniors' Book 3, to Clarendon Press.
The Tom Cat from 'Poems and Portraits' by Don Marquis. Copy-
   right 1917 by Sun Printing and Publishing Association.
   Reprinted by permission of Doubleday & Company Inc.
The Vagabond from Collected Poems of John Drinkwater and
   The Train from 'The Bridge' from 'Walls and Hedges' by
   John Redwood Anderson, to Sidgwick & Jackson Ltd.
Autumn Morning at Cambridge from Collected Poems of Frances
   Cornford, to The Cresset Press Ltd.
Wander-thirst from Collected Poems of Gerald Gould, to Michael
   Ayrton.
Sir Smasham Uppe by E. V. Rieu, from 'A Puffin Quartet of Poets'
   to the author.
There was an Indian from the 'Collected Poems' of Sir John Squire,
   to Mr Raglan Squire and Macmillan & Co. Ltd.
Nancy Hanks by Rosemary Benét from 'A Book of Americans',
   Rinehart and Company Inc., Copyright 1933, by Rosemary
   and Stephen Vincent Benét.
Spring from 'The Song of Solomon' and *Psalm 107* are from the
   text of the Authorised Version of the Bible which is Crown
   copyright, and the extracts taken from it are reproduced by
   permission.
A Ship Sails up to Bideford from 'Pillicock Hill' by Herbert Asquith,
   to William Heinemann Ltd.
Night Mail by W. H. Auden, to H.M. Postmaster General.
The Diver by W. W. E. Ross, from 'The Penguin Anthology of
   Canadian Verse', to the Author.

Contents

CONTENTS   Page

7

CONTENTS   Page

English

As gardens grow with flowers
English grows with words,
Words that have secret powers,
Words that give joy like birds.

Some of the words you say,
Both in and out of school,
Are brighter than the day
And deeper than a pool.

Some words there are that dance,
Some words there are that sigh,
The fool's words come by chance,
The poet's to heaven fly.

When you are grown, your tongue
Should give the joy of birds;
Get while you are young
The gift of English words.

ELEANOR FARJEON

Jabberwocky

'Twas brillig, and the slithy toves
Did gyre and gimble in the wabe;
All mimsy were the borogoves,
And the mome raths outgrabe.

'Beware the Jabberwock, my son!
The jaws that bite, the claws that catch!
Beware the Jubjub bird and shun
The frumious Bandersnatch!'

He took his vorpal sword in hand:
Long time the manxome foe he sought —
So rested he by the Tumtum tree
And stood awhile in thought.

And as in uffish thought he stood,
The Jabberwock, with eyes of flame,
Came whiffling through the tulgey wood,
And burbled as it came!

One, two! One, two! And through and through
The vorpal blade went snicker — snack!
He left it dead, and with its head
He went galumphing back.

'And hast thou slain the Jabberwock!
Come to my arms, my beamish boy!
O frabjous day! Callooh! Callay!'
He chortled in his joy.

'Twas brillig, and the slithy toves
Did gyre and gimble in the wabe;
All mimsy were the borogoves,
And the mome raths outgrabe.

LEWIS CARROLL

The Hen and the Carp

Once, in a roostery,
There lived a speckled hen, and when —
Ever she laid an egg this hen
Ecstatically cried:
'O progeny miraculous, particular spectaculous,
What a wonderful hen am I!'

Down in a pond nearby
Perchance a fat and broody carp
Was basking, but her ears were sharp —
She heard Dame Cackle cry:
'O progeny miraculous, particular spectaculous,
What a wonderful hen am I!'

'Ah, Cackle', bubbled she,
'For your single egg, O silly one,
I lay at least a million;
Suppose for each I cried:
'O progeny miraculous, particular spectaculous!'
What a hullaballoo there'd be!'

IAN SERRAILLIER

Marching Song

Far away in Nanga-noon
Lived an old and grey Baboon,
Ah-mi, Sulâni!
Once a Prince among his kind,
Now forsaken, left behind,
Feeble, lonely, all but blind:
Sulâni, ghar magleer.

Peaceful Tishnar came by night,
In the moonbeams cold and white;
Ah-mi, Sulâni!
'Far away from Nanga-noon,
Old and lonely, grey Baboon;
Is a journey for thee soon!
Sulâni, ghar magleer.

'Be not frightened, shut thine eye;
Comfort take, nor weep, nor sigh;
Solitary Tishnar's nigh!'
Sulâni, ghar magleer.

Old Baboon, he gravely did
All that peaceful Tishnar bid;
Ah-mi, Sulâni!
In the darkness cold and grim
Drew his blanket over him;
Closed his old eyes, sad and dim:
Sulâni, ghar magleer.

Talaheeti sul magloon
Olgar, ulgar Manga-noon;
Ah-mi, Sulâni !
Tishnar Sootli maltmahee,
Ganganareez soongalee,
Manni, Mulgar sang suwhee
Sulâni, ghar magleer.

WALTER DE LA MARE

(from 'The Three Royal Monkeys')

Uriconium

There was a man of Uriconium
Who played a primitive harmonium,
Inventing, to relieve his tedium,
Melodies high, low, and medium,
And standing on his Roman cranium
Amidst a bed of wild geranium,
Better known as pelargonium,
Since with odium his harmonium
Was received in Uriconium.

JAMES REEVES

The Song of the Little Hunter

Ere Mor the Peacock flutters, ere the Monkey People cry,
Ere Chil the Kite swoops down a furlong sheer,
Through the Jungle very softly flits a shadow and a sigh —
He is Fear, O Little Hunter, he is Fear!

13

Very softly down the glade runs a waiting, watching shade,
And the whisper spreads and widens far and near;
And the sweat is on thy brow, for he passes even now —
He is Fear, O Little Hunter, he is Fear!

Ere the moon has climbed the mountain, ere the rocks are
     ribbed with light,
Where the downward-dipping trails are dank and drear,
Comes a breathing hard behind thee — snuffle — snuffle
     through the night —
It is Fear, O Little Hunter, it is Fear!
On thy knees and draw the bow; bid the shrilling arrow go;
In the empty, mocking thicket plunge the spear;
But thy hands are loosed and weak, and the blood has left thy
     cheek —
It is Fear, O Little Hunter, it is Fear!

When the heat-cloud sucks the tempest, when the slivered
     pine-trees fall,
When the blinding, blearing rain-squalls lash and veer;
Through the war-gongs of the thunder rings a voice more loud
     than all —
It is Fear, O Little Hunter, it is Fear!
Now the spates are banked and deep; now the footless boulders
     leap —
Now the lightning shows each littlest leaf-rib clear —
But thy throat is shut and dried, and thy heart against thy side
Hammers: Fear, O Little Hunter — this is Fear!

RUDYARD KIPLING

The Tyger

Tyger! Tyger! burning bright
In the forests of the night,
What immortal hand or eye
Could frame thy fearful symmetry?

In what distant deeps or skies
Burnt the fire of thine eyes?
On what wings dare he aspire?
What the hand dare seize the fire?

And what shoulder, and what art,
Could twist the sinews of thy heart?
And, when thy heart began to beat,
What dread hand, and what dread feet?

What the hammer? What the chain?
In what furnace was thy brain?
What the anvil? What dread grasp
Dare its deadly terrors clasp?

When the stars threw down their spears,
And watered heaven with their tears,
Did He smile His work to see?
Did He who made the lamb make thee?

Tyger! Tyger! burning bright
In the forests of the night,
What immortal hand or eye
Dare frame thy fearful symmetry?

WILLIAM BLAKE

The Tom Cat

At midnight in the alley
A Tom-cat comes to wail,
And he chants the hate of a million years
As he swings his snaky tail.

Malevolent, bony, brindled,
Tiger and devil and bard,
His eyes are coals from the middle of Hell
And his heart is black and hard.

He twists and crouches and capers
And bares his curved sharp claws,
And he sings to the stars of the jungle nights,
Ere cities were, or laws.

Beast from a world primeval,
He and his leaping clan,
When the blotched red moon leers over the roofs,
Give voice to their scorn of man.

He will lie on a rug tomorrow
And lick his silky fur,
And veil the brute in his yellow eyes
And play he's tame, and purr.

But at midnight in the alley
He will crouch again and wail,
And beat the time for his demon's song
With the swing of his demon's tail.

DON MARQUIS

On a Night of Snow

Cat, if you go outdoors you must walk in the snow,
You will come back with little white shoes on your feet,
Little white slippers of snow that have heels of sleet.
Stay by the fire, my Cat. Lie still, do not go.
See how the flames are leaping and hissing low,
I will bring you a saucer of milk like a marguerite,
So white and so smooth, so spherical and so sweet —
Stay with me, Cat. Out-doors the wild winds blow.

Out-doors the wild winds blow, Mistress, and dark is the night.
Strange voices cry in the trees, intoning strange lore,
And more than cats move, lit by our eyes' green light,
On silent feet where the meadow grasses hang hoar —
Mistress, there are portents abroad of magic and might,
And things that are yet to be done. Open the door!

ELIZABETH J. COATSWORTH

The Eagle

He clasps the crag with crooked hands;
Close to the sun in lonely lands,
Ringed with the azure world he stands.

The wrinkled sea beneath him crawls;
He watches from his mountain walls,
And like a thunderbolt he falls.

ALFRED, LORD TENNYSON

The Eagle

He hangs between his wings outspread
Level and still
And bends a narrow golden head,
Scanning the ground to kill.

Though as he sails and smoothly swings
Round the hill side,
He looks as though from his own wings
He hung down crucified.

ANDREW YOUNG

Michael's Song

Because I set no snare
But leave them flying free,
All the birds of the air
Belong to me.

From the blue-tit on the sloe
To the eagle on the height,
Uncaged they come and go
For my delight.

And so the sunward way
I soar on the eagle's wings,
And in my heart all day
The blue-tit sings.

WILFRED GIBSON

The Canary

The song of canaries
Never varies,
And when they're moulting
They're pretty revolting

OGDEN NASH

The Vagabond

Give to me the life I love,
Let the lave go by me,
Give the jolly heaven above
And the byway nigh me.
Bed in the bush with stars to see,
Bread I dip in the river —
There's the life for a man like me,
There's the life for ever.

Let the blow fall soon or late,
Let what will be o'er me;
Give the face of earth around
And the road before me.
Wealth I seek not, hope nor love,
Nor a friend to know me;
All I seek, the heaven above,
And the road below me.

Or let autumn fall on me
Where afield I linger,
Silencing the bird on tree,
Biting the blue finger,
White as meal the frosty field —
Warm the fireside haven —
Not to autumn will I yield,
Not to winter even.

Let the blow fall soon or late,
Let what will be o'er me;
Give the face of earth around
And the road before me.
Wealth I ask not, hope nor love,
Nor a friend to know me;
All I ask, the heaven above,
And the road below me.

ROBERT LOUIS STEVENSON

The Vagabond

I know the pools where the grayling rise,
I know the trees where the filberts fall,
I know the woods where the red fox lies,
The twisted elms where the brown owls call.
And I've seldom a shilling to call my own,
And there's never a girl I'd marry,
I thank the Lord I am a rolling stone
With never a care to carry.

I talk to the stars as they come and go
On every night from July to June,
I'm free of the speech of the winds that blow,
And I know what weather will sing what tune.
I sow no seed and I pay no rent,
And I thank no man for his bounties,
But I've a treasure that's never spent,
I'm lord of a dozen counties.

JOHN DRINKWATER

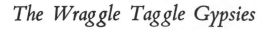

The Wraggle Taggle Gypsies

Three gypsies stood at the Castle gate,
They sang so high, they sang so low,
The lady sate in her chamber late,
Her heart it melted away as snow.

They sang so sweet, they sang so shrill,
That fast her tears began to flow.
And she laid down her silken gown,
Her golden rings and all her show.

She plucked off her high-heeled shoes,
A' made of Spanish leather, O!
She would in the street, with her bare, bare feet,
All out in the wind and weather, O!

It was late last night, when my lord came home,
Enquiring for his a-lady, O!
The servants said on every hand,
'She's gone with the wraggle taggle gypsies, O!'

'O saddle to me my milk-white steed.
Go and fetch me my pony, O!
That I may ride and seek my bride,
Who is gone with the wraggle taggle gypsies, O!'

O he rode high and he rode low,
He rode through woods and copses too.
Until he came to an open field,
And there he espied his a-lady, O!

'What makes you leave your house and land?
What makes you leave your money, O?
What makes you leave your new-wedded lord,
To go with the wraggle taggle gypsies, O?'

'What care I for my house and my land?
What care I for my money, O?
What care I for my new-wedded lord?
I'm off with the wraggle taggle gypsies, O!'

'Last night you slept on a goose-feather bed,
With the sheet turned down so bravely, O!
And tonight you'll sleep in a cold open field,
Along with the wraggle taggle gypsies, O!'

'What care I for a goose-feather bed,
With the sheet turned down so bravely, O?
For tonight I shall sleep in a cold open field,
Along with the wraggle taggle gypsies, O!'

TRADITIONAL

Meg Merrilies

Old Meg she was a Gipsy
And lived upon the moors;
Her bed it was the brown heath turf,
Her house was out of doors.

Her apples were swart blackberries,
Her currants pods o' broom;
Her wine was dew of the wild white rose,
Her book a churchyard tomb.

Her brothers were the craggy hills,
Her sisters larchen trees.
Alone with her great family
She lived as she did please.

No breakfast had she many a morn,
No dinner many a noon,
And 'stead of supper she would stare
Full hard against the moon.

But every morn of woodbine fresh
She made her garlanding,
And every night the dark glen yew
She wove, and she would sing.

And with her fingers old and brown
She plaited mats o' rushes,
And gave them to the cottagers,
She met among the bushes.

Old Meg was brave as Margaret Queen
And tall as Amazon:
An old red blanket cloak she wore,
A chip hat had she on.
God rest her aged bones somewhere —
She died full long agone!

JOHN KEATS

In a Cornfield

A silence of full noontide heat
Grew on them at their toil.
The farmer's dog woke up from sleep,
The green snake hid her coil
Where grass grew thickest; bird and beast
Sought shadows as they could,
The reaping men and women paused
And sat down where they stood;
They ate and drank and were refreshed,
For rest from toil is good.

CHRISTINA ROSSETTI

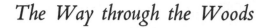

The Way through the Woods

They shut the road through the woods
Seventy years ago.
Weather and rain have undone it again,
And now you would never know
There was once a road through the woods
Before they planted the trees.
It is underneath the coppice and heath,
And the thin anemones.
Only the keeper sees
That, where the ring-dove broods,
And the badgers roll at ease,
There was once a road through the woods.

Yet, if you enter the woods
Of a summer evening, late,
When the night-air cools on the trout-ringed pools
Where the otter whistles his mate,
(They fear not men in the woods,
Because they see so few,)
You will hear the beat of a horse's feet,
And the swish of a skirt in the dew,
Steadily cantering through
The misty solitudes,
As though they perfectly knew
The old lost road through the woods . . .
But there is no road through the woods.

RUDYARD KIPLING

Autumn Morning at Cambridge

I ran out in the morning, when the air was clean and new
And all the grass was glittering and grey with autumn dew,
I ran out to an apple-tree and pulled an apple down,
And all the bells were ringing in the old grey town.

Down in the town off the bridges and the grass,
They are sweeping up the leaves to let the people pass,
Sweeping up the old leaves, golden-reds and browns,
Whilst the men go to lecture with the wind in their gowns.

FRANCES CORNFORD

Wind and Silver

Greatly shining
The Autumn moon floats in the thin sky;
And the fish-ponds shake their backs and
    flash their dragon scales
As she passes over them.

AMY LOWELL

The Fog

I saw the fog grow thick,
Which soon made blind my ken;
It made tall men of boys,
And giants of tall men.

It clutched my throat, I coughed;
Nothing was in my head
Except two heavy eyes
Like balls of burning lead.

And when it grew so black
That I could know no place,
I lost all judgment then,
Of distance and of space.

The street lamps, and the lights
Upon the halted cars,
Could either be the earth
Or be the heavenly stars.

A man passed by me close,
I asked my way; he said
'Come, follow me, my friend' —
I followed where he led.

He rapped the stones in front,
'Trust me,' he said 'and come.'
I followed like a child —
A blind man led me home.

W. H. DAVIES

Snow in the Suburbs

Every branch big with it,
Bent every twig with it;
Every fork like a white web-foot;
Every street and pavement mute:
Some flakes have lost their way, and grope back upwards,
                                                    when
Meeting those meandering down they turn and descend again.
The palings are glued together like a wall,
And there is no waft of wind with the fleecy fall.

A sparrow enters the tree,
Whereupon immediately
A snow-lump thrice his own slight size
Descends on him and showers his head and eyes,
And overturns him,
And near inurns him,
And lights on a nether twig when its brush
Starts off a volley of other lodging lumps with a rush.

The steps are a branched shape
Up which, with feeble hope,
A black cat comes, wide-eyed and thin;
And we take him in.

THOMAS HARDY

The Snowflake

Before I melt,
Come, look at me!
This lovely icy filigree!
Of a great forest
In one night
I make a wilderness
Of white:
By skyey cold
Of crystal made,
All softly, on
Your finger laid,
I pause, that you
My beauty see:
Breathe, and I vanish
Instantly.

WALTER DE LA MARE

Ice

The North Wind sighed:
And in a trice
What was water
Now is ice.

What sweet rippling
Water was
Now bewitched is
Into glass:

White and brittle
Where is seen
The prisoned milfoil's
Tender green;

Clear and ringing
With sun aglow,
Where the boys sliding
And skating go.

Now furred's each stick
And stalk and blade
With crystals out of
Dewdrops made.

Worms and ants,
Flies, snails and bees
Keep close house guard,
Lest they freeze;

O with how sad
And solemn an eye
Each fish stares up
Into the sky

In dread lest his
Wide watery home
At night shall solid
Ice become.

WALTER DE LA MARE

Winter the Huntsman

Through his iron glades
Rides Winter the Huntsman.
All colour fades
As his horn is heard sighing.

For through the forest
His wild hooves crash and thunder
Till many a mighty branch
Is torn asunder.

And the red reynard creeps
To his hole near the river,
The copper leaves fall
And the bare trees shiver.

As night creeps from the ground,
Hides each tree from its brother,
And each dying sound
Reveals yet another.

Is it Winter the Huntsman
Who gallops through his iron glades,
Cracking his cruel whip
To the gathering shades?

OSBERT SITWELL

Blow, Blow, thou Winter Wind

Blow, blow, thou winter wind,
Thou art not so unkind
As man's ingratitude;
Thy tooth is not so keen,
Because thou art not seen,
Although thy breath be rude.

Heigh-ho! sing, heigh-ho! unto the green holly:
Most friendship is feigning, most loving mere folly.
    Then heigh-ho! the holly!
    This life is most jolly.

Freeze, freeze, thou bitter sky,
That dost not bite so nigh
As benefits forgot.
Though thou the waters warp,
Thy sting is not so sharp
As friend remembered not.

Heigh-ho! sing heigh-ho! unto the green holly:
Most friendship is feigning, most loving mere folly.
    Then heigh-ho! the holly!
    This life is most jolly.

WILLIAM SHAKESPEARE

Up in the morning's no' for me

Up in the morning's no for me,
Up in the morning early;
When a' the hills are covered wi' snaw
I'm sure it's winter fairly.

Cauld blaws the wind frae east to west,
The drift is driving sairly;
Sae loud and shrill I hear the blast,
I'm sure it's winter fairly.

The birds sit chattering in the thorn,
A' day they fare but sparely;
And long's the night frae e'en to morn;
I'm sure it's winter fairly.

ROBERT BURNS

After the Storm

There was a roaring in the wind all night;
The rain came heavily and fell in floods;
But now the sun is rising calm and bright;
The birds are singing in the distant woods;
Over his own sweet voice the Stock-dove broods;
The Jay makes answer as the Magpie chatters;
And all the air is filled with pleasant noise of waters.

All things that love the sun are out of doors;
The sky rejoices in the morning's birth;
The grass is bright with rain drops; on the moors
The hare is running races in her mirth;
And with her feet she from the plashy earth
Raises a mist; that, glittering in the sun,
Runs with her all the way, wherever she doth run.

WILLIAM WORDSWORTH

Spring

For lo, the winter is past, the rain is over and gone;

The flowers appear on the earth, the time of the singing, of birds
is come, and the voice of the turtle is heard in our land.

The fig tree putteth forth her green figs, and the vines with the
tender grape give a good smell. Arise, my love, my fair one, and
come away.

from THE SONG OF SOLOMON

Sir Lancelot

A bow-shot from her bower-eaves
He rode between the barley sheaves,
The sun came dazzling thro' the leaves
And flamed upon the brazen greaves
    Of bold Sir Lancelot.
A red-cross knight forever kneel'd
To a lady in his shield
That sparkled on the yellow field
    Beside remote Shalott.

The gemmy bridle glittered free,
Like to some branch of stars we see
Hung in the golden Galaxy.
The bridle bells rang merrily
    As he rode down to Camelot;
And from his blazon'd baldric slung
A mighty silver bugle hung,
And as he rode his armour rung,
    Beside remote Shalott.

All in the blue unclouded weather
Thick-jewell'd shone the saddle-leather,
The helmet and the helmet-feather
Burn'd like one burning flame together
    As he rode down to Camelot.
As often thro' the purple night,
Below the starry clusters bright,
Some bearded meteor, trailing light,
    Moves over still Shalott.

His broad clear brow in sunlight glow'd;
On burnish'd hooves his war-horse trode;
From underneath his helmet flow'd
His coal black curls as on he rode,
    As he rode down to Camelot.
From the bank and from the river
He flashed into the crystal mirror,
'Tirra lirra,' by the river
    Sang Sir Lancelot.

ALFRED, LORD TENNYSON

from 'The Lady of Shalott'.

Rain

I woke in the swimming dark
And heard, now sweet, now shrill,
The voice of the rain-water,
Cold and still.

Endlessly sing; now faint,
In the distance borne away;
Now in the air float near,
But nowhere stay.

Singing I know not what,
Echoing on and on;
Following me to sleep,
Till night was gone.

WALTER DE LA MARE

The Train

Out of the silence grows
An iron thunder — grows, and roars, and sweeps,
Menacing! The plain
Suddenly leaps,
Startled, from its repose —
Alert and listening. Now from the gloom
Of the soft distance loom
Three lights and, over them, a brush

Of tawny flame and flying spark —
Three pointed lights that rush,
Monstrous, upon the cringing dark.
And nearer, nearer rolls the sound,
Louder the throb and roar of wheels,
The shout of speed, the shriek of steam;
The sloping bank,
Cut into flashing squares, gives back the clank
And grind of metal, while the ground
Shudders and the bridge reels —
As, with a scream,
The train,

A rage of smoke, a laugh of fire,
A lighted anguish of desire,
A dream
Of gold and iron, of sound and flight,
Tumultuous roars across the night.

J. REDWOOD ANDERSON
from 'The Bridge'.

The Train

A green eye — and a red — in the dark,
Thunder — smoke — and a spark.

It is there — it is here — flashed by.
Whither will the wild thing fly?

It is rushing, tearing through the night,
Rending her gloom in its flight.

It shatters her silence with shrieks.
What is it the wild thing seeks?

Alas, for it hurries away
Them that are fain to stay.

Hurrah! for it carries home
Lovers and friends that roam.

MARY COLERIDGE

Night Mail

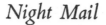

This is the night mail crossing the border,
Bringing the cheque and the postal order,
Letters for the rich, letters for the poor,
The shop at the corner and the girl next door.
Pulling up Beattock, a steady climb —
The gradient's against her, but she's on time.

Past cotton grass and moorland boulder,
Shovelling white steam over her shoulder,
Snorting noisily as she passes
Silent miles of wind-bent grasses.
Birds turn their heads as she approaches,
Stare from the bushes at her blank-faced coaches.
Sheepdogs cannot turn her course,
They slumber on with paws across.
In the farm she passes no one wakes,
But a jug in the bedroom gently shakes.

Dawn freshens, the climb is done.
Down towards Glasgow she descends
Towards the steam tugs yelping down the glade of cranes,
Towards the fields of apparatus, the furnaces
Set on the dark plain like gigantic chessmen.
All Scotland waits for her:
In the dark glen, beside the pale-green lochs,
Men long for news.

Letters of thanks, letters from banks,
Letters of joy from girl and boy,
Receipted bills, and invitations
To inspect new stock or visit relations,
And applications for situations
And timid lovers' declarations
And gossip, gossip from all the nations,
News circumstantial, news financial,
Letters with holiday snaps to enlarge in,
Letters with faces scrawled in the margin,
Letters from uncles, cousins and aunts,
Letters to Scotland from the South of France,
Letters of condolence to Highlands and Lowlands,
Written on paper of every hue,
The pink, the violet, the white and the blue,
The chatty, the catty, the boring, adoring,
The cold and official and the heart's outpouring.
Clever, stupid, short and long,
The typed and the printed and the spelt all wrong.

Thousands are still asleep
Dreaming of terrifying monsters,
Or a friendly tea beside the band at Cranston's or Crawford's:
Asleep in working Glasgow, asleep in well-set Edinburgh,
Asleep in granite Aberdeen,
They continue their dreams;
But shall wake soon and long for letters,
And none will hear the postman's knock
Without a quickening of the heart,
For who can hear and feel himself forgotten?

                                        W. H. AUDEN

The Listeners

'Is there anybody there?' said the Traveller,
Knocking on the moonlit door:
And his horse in the silence champed the grasses
Of the forest's ferny floor:
And a bird flew up out of the turret,
Above the Traveller's head.
And he smote upon the door again a second time;
'Is there anybody there?' he said.
But no one descended to the Traveller,
No head from the leaf-fringed sill
Leaned over and looked into his grey eyes,
Where he stood perplexed and still.
But only a host of phantom listeners
That dwelt in the lone house then
Stood listening in the quiet of the moonlight
To that voice from the world of men:
Stood thronging the faint moonbeams on the dark stair,
That goes down to the empty hall,
Harkening in an air stirred and shaken
By the lonely Traveller's call.
And he felt in his heart their strangeness,
Their stillness answering his cry,
While his horse moved, cropping the dark turf,
'Neath the starred and leafy sky;
For he suddenly smote on the door, even
Louder, and lifted his head:
'Tell them I came, and no one answered,
That I kept my word,' he said.

Never the least stir made the listeners,
Though every word he spake
Fell echoing through the shadowiness of the still house
From the one man left awake:
Ay, they heard his foot upon the stirrup,
And the sound of iron on stone,
And how the silence surged softly backward,
When the plunging hoofs were gone.

WALTER DE LA MARE

Nancy Hanks

If Nancy Hanks
Came back as a ghost,
Seeking news
Of what she loved most,
She'd ask first
'Where's my son?
What's happened to Abe?
What's he done?'

'Poor little Abe,
Left all alone,
Except for Tom,
Who's a rolling stone.
He was only nine
The year I died.
I remember still
How hard he cried.

'Scraping along
In a little shack
With hardly a shirt
To cover his back,
And a prairie wind
To blow him down,
Or pinching times
If he went to town.

'You wouldn't know
About my son?
Did he grow tall?
Did he have fun?
Did he learn to read?
Did he get to town?
Do you know his name?
Did he get on?'

ROSEMARY BENÉT

The Strange Visitor

A wife was sitting at her reel ae night;
And aye she sat, and aye she reeled, and aye she wished for
    company.

In came a pair o' braid braid soles, and sat down at the fireside;
And aye she sat, and aye she reeled, and aye she wished for
    company.

In came a pair o' sma' legs, and sat down on the braid braid
    soles;
And aye she sat, and aye she reeled, and aye she wished for
    company.

In came a pair o' muckle muckle knees, and sat down on the
    sma' sma' legs;
And aye she sat, an aye she reeled, and aye she wished for
    company.

In came a pair o' sma' sma' thecs, and sat down on the muckle
    muckle knees;
And aye she sat, and aye she reeled, and aye she wished for
    company.

In came a pair o' muckle muckle hips, and sat down on the
    sma' sma' thees;
And aye she sat, and aye she reeled, and aye she wished for
    company.

In came a sma' sma' waist, and sat down on the muckle muckle
    hips;
And aye she sat, and aye she reeled, and aye she wished for
    company.

In came a pair o' braid braid shouthers, and sat down on the
    sma' sma' waist;
And aye she sat, and aye she reeled, and aye she wished for
    company.

In came a pair o' sma' sma' arms, and sat down on the braid
    braid shouthers;
And aye she sat, and aye she reeled, and aye she wished for
    company.

In came a pair o' muckle muckle hands, and sat down on the
    sma' sma' arms;
And aye she sat, and aye she reeled, and aye she wished for
    company.

In came a sma' sma' neck, and sat down on the braid braid
    shouthers;
And aye she sat, and aye she reeled, and aye she wished for
    company.

In came a great big head, and sat down on the sma' sma' neck;
And aye she sat, and aye she reeled, and aye she wished for
    company.

'What way hae ye sic braid braid feet?' quo' the wife.
'Muckle ganging, muckle ganging.'
'What way hae ye sic sma' sma' legs?'
'*Aih-h-h*! — late — and *wee-e-e* moul'
'What way hae ye sic muckle muckle knees?'
'Muckle praying, muckle praying.'
'What way hae ye sic sma' sma' thees?'
'*Aih-h-h*! — late — and *wee-e-e* moul.'
'What way hae ye sic big big hips?'
'Muckle sitting, muckle sitting.'
'What way hae ye sic a sma' sma' waist?'
'*Aih-h-h*! — late — and *wee-e-e* moul.'
'What way hae ye sic braid braid shouthers?'
'Wi' carrying broom, wi' carrying broom.'
'What way hae ye sic muckle muckle hands?'
'Threshing wi' an iron flail, threshing wi' an iron flail.'
'What way hae ye sic a sma' sma' neck?'
'*Aih-h-h*! — late — and *wee-e-e* moul.'
'What way hae ye sic a muckle muckle head?'
'Muckle wit, muckle wit.'
'What do you come for?'
'For YOU!'

TRADITIONAL ·

The Wife of Usher's Well

There lived a wife at Usher's Well,
And a wealthy wife was she;
She had three stout and stalwart sons,
And sent them o'er the sea.

They hadna been a week from her,
A week but barely one,
When word came to the carline wife
That her three sons were gone.

They hadna been a week from her,
A week but barely three,
When word came to the carline wife
That her sons she'd never see.

'I wish the wind may never cease,
Nor fashes in the flood,
Till my three sons come hame to me
In earthly flesh and blood.'

It fell about the Martinmas,
When nights are lang and mirk,
The carline wife's three sons came hame,
And their hats were o' the birk.

It neither grew in syke nor ditch,
Nor yet in any sheugh;
But at the gates o' Paradise
That birk grew fair enough.

'Blow up the fire, my maidens,
Bring water from the well;
For a' my house shall feast this night,
Since my three sons are well.'

And she has made to them a bed,
She's made it large and wide,
And she's ta'en her mantle her about
Sat down at the bedside.

Up then crew the red, red cock,
And up and crew the grey;
The eldest to the youngest said,
'Tis time we were away.'

The cock he hadna crawed but once,
And clapped his wings at a',
When the youngest to the eldest said,
'Brother, we must awa'.'

'The cock doth craw, the day doth daw,
The channerin' worm doth chide;
Gin we be missed out o' our place,
A sair pain we maun bide.'

'Fare ye weel, my mother dear!
Fareweel to barn and byre!
And fare ye weel, the bonny lass
That kindles my mother's fire.'

TRADITIONAL

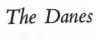

The Danes

Their sails, as black as a starless night,
Came moving on, with a sullen might;
Rows of gleaming shields there hung,
Over the gunwales in order slung;
And the broad black banners fluttered and flapped
Like raven's pinions, as dipped and lapped
The Norsemen's galleys; their axes shone.

Every Dane had a hauberk on —
Glittering gold; how each robber lord
Waved in the air his threatening sword!
One long swift rush through surf and foam
And they leapt, ere the rolling wave had gone,
On our Saxon shore, their new-found home.

GEORGE WALTER THORNBURY

There was an Indian

There was an Indian who had known no change,
Who strayed content along a sunlit beach
Gathering shells. He heard a sudden strange
Commingled noise: looked up; and gasped for speech.

For in the bay, where nothing was before,
Moved on the sea, by magic, huge canoes
With bellying cloths on poles, and not one oar,
And fluttering coloured signs and clambering crews.

And he, in fear, this naked man alone,
His fallen hands forgetting all their shells,
His lips gone pale, knelt low behind a stone,
And stared, and saw, and did not understand,
Columbus's doom-burdened caravels
Slant to the shore, and all their seamen land.

SIR JOHN SQUIRE

Dunkirk 1940

The little ships, the little ships
Rushed out across the sea
To save the luckless armies
From death and slavery.

From Tyne and Thames and Tamar,
From the Severn and the Clyde,
The little ships, the little ships
Went out in all their pride —

And home they brought their warriors,
Weary and ragged and worn,
Back to the hills and shires
And the towns where they were born.

Three hundred thousand warriors,
From Hell to Home they came,
In the little ships, the little ships
Of everlasting fame.

IDRIS DAVIES

A Ship Sails up to Bideford

A ship sails up to Bideford
Upon a western breeze,
Mast by mast, sail over sail,
She rises from the seas,
And sights the hills of Devon
And the misty English trees.

She comes from Eastern islands;
The sun is on her hold;
She bears the fruit of Jaffa,
Dates, oranges and gold;

She brings the silk of China,
And bales of Persian dyes,
And birds with sparkling feathers,
And snakes with diamond eyes.

She's gliding in the sunlight
As white as any gull;
The East is gliding with her
In the shadows of her hull.

A ship sails up to Bideford
Upon a western breeze,
With fruits of eastern summers
She rises from the seas,
And sights the hills of Devon
And the misty English trees.

HERBERT ASQUITH

Smells

Why is it that the poets tell
So little of the sense of smell?
These are the odours I love well:

The smell of coffee, freshly ground;
Or rich plum pudding, holly-crowned;
Or onions fried and deeply browned.

The fragrance of a fumy pipe;
The smell of apples, newly ripe;
And printers' ink on leaden type.

Woods by moonlight in September
Breathe most sweet; and I remember
Many a smoky camp-fire ember.

Camphor, turpentine, and tea,
The balsam of a Christmas tree,
These are whiffs of gramarye —
A ship smells best of all to me!

CHRISTOPHER MORLEY

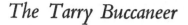

The Tarry Buccaneer

I'm going to be a pirate with a bright brass pivot-gun,
And an island in the Spanish Main beyond the setting sun,
And a silver flagon full of red wine to drink when work is
    done,
Like a fine old salt-sea scavenger, like a tarry Buccaneer.

With a sandy creek to careen in, and a pig-tailed Spanish mate,
And under my main hatches a sparkling merry freight
Of doubloons and double moidores and pieces of eight,
Like a fine old salt-sea scavenger, like a tarry Buccaneer.

With a taste for Spanish wine-shops and for spending my
    doubloons,
And a crew of swart mulattoes and black-eyed octoroons,
And a thoughtful way with mutineers of making them
    maroons,
Like a fine old salt-sea scavenger, like a tarry Buccaneer.

With a sash of crimson velvet and a diamond-hilted sword,
And a silver whistle about my neck secured to a golden cord,
And a habit of taking captives and walking them along a
    board,
Like a fine old salt-sea scavenger, like a tarry Buccaneer.

With a spy-glass tucked beneath my arm and a cocked hat
    cocked askew,
And a long, low, rakish schooner a–cutting of the waves in
    two,
And a flag of skull and crossbones the wickedest that ever flew,
Like a tine old salt-sea scavenger, like a tarry Buccaneer.

JOHN MASEFIELD

Trade Winds

In the harbour, in the island, in the Spanish Seas,
Are the tiny white houses and the orange trees,
And day-long, night-long, the cool and pleasant breeze
    Of the steady Trade Winds blowing.

There is the red wine, the nutty Spanish ale,
The shuffle of the dancers, the old salt's tale,
The squeaking fiddle, and the soughing in the sail
    Of the steady Trade Winds blowing.

And o' nights there's fire-flies and the yellow moon,
And in the ghostly palm-trees the sleepy tune
Of the quiet voice calling me, the long low croon
    Of the steady Trade Winds blowing.

JOHN MASEFIELD

The Ship

They have launched the little ship,
She is riding by the quay.
Like a young doe to the river,
She has trembled to the sea.

Her sails are shaken loose;
They flutter in the wind.
The cats-paws ripple round her
And the gulls scream behind.

The rope is cast, she moves
Daintily out and south,
Where the snarling ocean waits her
With tiger-foaming mouth.

RICHARD CHURCH

The Water Snakes

Beyond the shadow of the ship
I watched the water snakes.
They moved in tracks of shining white
And when they reared, the elfish light
Fell off in hoary flakes.

Within the shadow of the ship
I watched their rich attire
Blue, glossy green, and velvet black,
They coiled and swam, and every track
Was a flash of golden fire.

S. T. COLERIDGE

from 'The Rime of the Ancient Mariner'

Psalm 107

They that go down to the sea in ships, that do business in
    great waters;
These see the works of the Lord, and His wonders in the deep.
For He commandeth, and raiseth the stormy wind, which lift-
    eth up the waves thereof.
They mount up to the heaven, they go down again to the
    depths: their soul is melted because of trouble.
They reel to and fro, and stagger like a drunken man, and are
    at their wits' end.
Then they cry unto the Lord in their trouble, and He bringeth
    them out of their distresses.
He maketh the storm a calm, so that the waves thereof are still.
Then are they glad because they be quiet; so he bringeth them
    unto their desired haven.

Fish in Pacific Waters

Then did Ocean,
The great showman, out of the bountiful deep
Conjure all manner of strange creatures
To delight them: flying fish that shot through the air
Like quicksilver, smack against the sail,
Then dropped to deck into the breakfast saucepan
Waiting there; the prosperous tunny,
Fat as an alderman with rows of double chins;
The glorious dolphin, bluebottle-green
With glittering golden fins, greedy
For the succulent weed that trailed like garlands
From the steering oar. There were many more —
Take the blue shark, a glutton
For blood; he'd swallow a dolphin, bones and all,
And crunch them like a concrete-mixer. They learnt
How to fool him with tit-bits, to get him
By his tail and haul aboard, skipping
Quickly from the snapping jaw —
He'd make a meal of anyone who let him!
(Rare sport this for the parrot who
For safety flew to the roof of the raft
And shrieked at the fun of it, and laughed and laughed).
Every kind they saw, from the million pilot fish
Tiny as a finger nail
To the majestic tremendous spotted whale,
Long as a tennis-court, who could —
Were he so minded — with one flick of his great tail
Have swatted them flat as a fly. But he couldn't be bothered.
Instead, circling cumbrously below,

He scratched his lazy back on the steering oar,
Till Erik sent him packing
With half a foot of steel in his spine.
Deep down he plunged, and the harpoon line —
Whipping through their hands — snapped like twine.

IAN SERRAILLIER

from 'The Ballad of Kon Tiki'

The Kraken

Below the thunders of the upper deep;
Far, far beneath in the abysmal sea,
His ancient, dreamless, uninvaded sleep
The Kraken sleepeth; faintest sunlights flee
About his shadowy sides: above him swell
Huge sponges of millennial growth and height;
And far away into the sickly light,
From many a wondrous grot and secret cell
Unnumber'd and enormous polypi
Winnow with giant arms the slumbering green.
There hath he lain for ages and will lie
Battening upon huge seaworms in his sleep
Until the latter fire shall heat the deep;
Then once by man and angels to be seen,
In roaring he shall rise and on the surface die.

ALFRED, LORD TENNYSON

The Diver

I would like to dive
Down
Into this still pool
Where the rocks at the bottom are safely deep,

Into the green
Of the water seen from within,
A strange light
Streaming past my eyes —

Things hostile,
You cannot stay here, they seem to say;
The rocks, slime-covered, the undulating
Fronds of weeds —

And drift slowly
Among the cooler zones;
Then, upward turning,
Break from the green glimmer

Into the light
White and ordinary of the day,
And the mild air,
With the breeze and the comfortable shore.

W. W. E. ROSS

Sir Patrick Spens

The King sits in Dunfermline town
Drinking the blude-red wine;
'O where will I get a skeely skipper
To sail this new ship o' mine?'

O up and spak an eldern knight,
Sat at the King's right knee:
'Sir Patrick Spens is the best sailor
That ever sail'd the sea.'

Our king has written a braid letter,
And sealed it with his hand,
And sent it to Sir Patrick Spens,
Was walking on the strand.

'To Noroway, to Noroway,
To Noroway o'er the faem;
The king's daughter of Noroway,
'Tis thou must bring her hame.'

The first word that Sir Patrick read
So loud loud laughed he;
The neist word that Sir Patrick read
The tear blinded his e'e.

'O wha is this has done this deed
And tauld the king o' me,
To send us out at this time o' the year,
To sail upon the sea?

'Be it wind, be it weet, be it hail, be it sleet,
Our ship must sail the faem;
The king's daughter of Noroway
'Tis we must fetch her hame.'

They hoysed their sails on Monenday morn
W' a' the speed they may;
They hae landed in Noroway
Upon a Wodensday.

They hadna been a week, a week
In Noroway, but twae
When that the lords o' Noroway
Began aloud to say:

'Ye Scottish men spend a' our king's gold
And a' our queene's fee.'
'Ye lie, ye lie, ye liars loud,
Fu' loud I hear ye lie,

'For I have brought as much white money
As gone my men and me,
And I have brought of good red gold
Out o'er the sea with me.

'Make ready, make ready my merry men a'!
Our gude ship sails the morn.'
'Now, ever alack, my master dear,
I fear a deadly storm.

'I saw the new moon late yestreen
Wi' the auld moon in her arm;
And if we gang to sea, master,
I fear we'll come to harm.'

They hadna sailed a league, a league,
A league but barely three,
When the lift grew dark, and the wind blew loud,
And gurly grew the sea.

The ankers brake and the topmasts lap.
It was sic a deadly storm;
And the waves came o'er the broken ship
Till a' her sides were torn.

'O where will I get a gude sailor
To take my helm in hand,
Till I get up to the tall topmast
To see if I can spy land?'

'O here am I, a sailor gude,
To take the helm in hand,
Till you go up to the tall topmast,
But I fear you'll ne'er spy land.'

He hadna gane a step, a step,
A step but hardly ane,
When a bolt flew out of our goodly ship,
And the salt sea it came in.

'Go fetch a web o' the silken claith,
Another o' the twine,
And wap them into our ship's side,
And let na the sea come in.'

They fetched a web o' the silken claith,
Another o' the twine,
And they wapped them round that gude ship's side,
But still the sea came in.

O laith, laith were our gude Scots lords
To wet their cork-heeled shoon,
But lang or a' the play was played
They wat their hats aboon.

And mony was the feather bed
That floated on the faem;
And mony was the gude lord's son
That never mair came hame.

The ladies wrang their fingers white,
The maidens tore their hair;
A' for the sake of their true loves,
For them they'll see na mair.

O lang lang may the ladies sit,
Wi' their fans into their hand
Before they see Sir Patrick Spens
Come sailing to the strand!

And lang lang may the maidens sit
Wi' their gowd kames in their hair,
A' waiting for their ain dear loves —
For them they'll see na mair.

Half-owre, half-owre, to Aberdour
'Tis fifty fathoms deep,
And there lies gude Sir Patrick Spens,
Wi' the Scots lords at his feet!

TRADITIONAL

Lord Ullin's Daughter

A chieftain to the Highlands bound
Cries 'Boatman, do not tarry!
And I'll give thee a silver pound
To row us o'er the ferry!'

'Now who be ye would cross Lochgyle,
This dark and stormy water?'
'O I'm the chief of Ulva's isle,
And this, Lord Ullin's daughter.

PAL4—E

'And fast before her father's men
Three days we've fled together,
For, should they find us in the glen,
My blood would stain the heather.

'His horsemen hard behind us ride —
Should they our steps discover,
Then who will cheer my bonny bride
When they have slain her lover?'

Out spoke the hardy Highland wight,
'I'll go, my chief, I'm ready:
It is not for your silver bright,
But for your winsome lady: —

'And, by my word! the song bird
In danger shall not tarry:
So though the waves are raging white
I'll row you o'er the ferry.'

By this the storm grew loud apace,
The water-wraith was shrieking;
And in the scowl of heaven each face
Grew dark as they were speaking.

But still, as wilder blew the wind,
And as the night grew drearer,
Adown the glen rode armed men,
Their trampling sounded nearer.

'O haste thee, haste!' the lady cries,
'Though tempests round us gather;
I'll meet the raging of the skies,
But not an angry father.'

The boat has left a stormy land,
A stormy sea before her —
When oh! too strong for human hand,
The tempest gather'd o'er her.

And still they row'd, amidst the roar
Of waters fast prevailing.
Lord Ullin reached that fatal shore —
His wrath was changed to wailing.

For, sore dismay'd, through storm and shade
His child he did discover —
One lovely hand she stretch'd for aid,
And one was round her lover.

'Come back! come back!' he cried in grief,
'Across this stormy water:
And I'll forgive your Highland chief,
My daughter! — O my daughter!'

'Twas vain: the loud waves lashed the shore,
Return or aid preventing:
The waters wild went o'er his child,
And he was left lamenting.

THOMAS CAMPBELL

Lochinvar

O, Young Lochinvar is come out of the west,
Through all the wide Border his steed was the best,
And save his good broadsword he weapons had none,
He rode all unarm'd, and he rode all alone.
So faithful in love, and so dauntless in war,
There never was knight like the young Lochinvar.

He staid not for brake and he stopp'd not for stone.
He swam the Eske river where ford there was none;
But ere he alighted at Netherby gate,
The bride had consented, the gallant came late;
For a laggard in love, and a dastard in war,
Was to wed the fair Ellen of brave Lochinvar.

So boldly he enter'd the Netherby Hall,
Among bride's-men, and kinsmen, and brothers, and all.
Then spake the bride's father, his hand on his sword,
(For the poor craven bridegroom said never a word),
'O come ye to peace here, or come ye in war,
Or to dance at our bridal, young Lord Lochinvar?'

'I long woo'd your daughter, my suit you denied;
Love swells like the Solway, but ebbs like its tide —
And now am I come, with this lost love of mine
To lead but one measure, drink one cup of wine.
There are maidens in Scotland more lovely by far,
That would gladly be bride to the young Lochinvar.'

The bride kiss'd the goblet: the knight took it up.
He quaff'd off the wine, and he threw down the cup.
She look'd down to blush, and she look'd up to sigh,
With a smile on her lips, and a tear in her eye.
He took her soft hand ere her mother could bar —
'Now tread me a measure!' said young Lochinvar.

So stately his form, and so lovely her face,
That never a hall such a galliard did grace;
While her mother did fret, and her father did fume,
And the bridegroom stood dangling his bonnet and plume;
And the bride-maidens whispered, ' 'Twere better by far,
To have match'd our fair cousin with young Lochinvar.'

One touch to her hand, and one word in her ear,
When they reach'd the hall-door, and the charger stood near.
So light to the croupe the fair lady he swung,
So light to the saddle before her he sprung.
'She is won! we are gone, over bank, bush, and scour;
They'll have fleet steeds that follow,' quoth young Lochinvar.

There was mounting 'mong Graemes of the Netherby clan;
Forsters, Fenwicks, and Musgraves, they rode and they ran;
There was racing and chasing on Cannobie Lee,
But the lost bride of Netherby ne'er did they see.
So daring in love, and so dauntless in war,
Have ye e'er heard of gallant like young Lochinvar?

SIR WALTER SCOTT

Auld Lang Syne

Should auld acquaintance be forgot,
And never brought to mind?
Should auld acquaintance be forgot,
And auld lang syne?
    For auld lang syne, my dear,
    For auld lang syne,
    We'll tak a cup o' kindness yet
    For auld lang syne!

And surely you'll be your pint stoup,
And surely I'll be mine;
And we'll tak' a cup o' kindness yet
For auld lang syne!

We twa hae run about the braes,
And pu'd the gowans fine;
But we've wandered mony a weary fit
Sin auld lang syne!

We twa hae paddléd in the burn,
Frae morning sun till dine;
But seas between us braid hae roar'd
Sin auld lang syne!

And there's a hand, my trusty fiere,
And gie's a hand o' thine;
And we'll tak a right guid-willie waught
For auld lang syne.

ROBERT BURNS

70

Home-thoughts, from Abroad

O to be in England
Now that April's there,
And whoever wakes in England
Sees, some morning, unaware,
That the lowest boughs and the brushwood sheaf
Round the elm-tree bole are in tiny leaf,
While the chaffinch sings on the orchard bough
In England — now!

And after April; when May follows,
And the whitethroat builds, and all the swallows!
Hark, where my blossom'd pear-tree in the hedge
Leans to the field and scatters on the clover
Blossoms and dewdrops — at the bent spray's edge —
That's the wise thrush; he sings each song twice over
Lest you should think he never could recapture
The first fine careless rapture!
And though the fields look rough with hoary dew,
All will be gay when noontide wakes anew
The buttercups, the little children's dower
Far brighter than this gaudy melon-flower!

ROBERT BROWNING

Puck's Song

See you the dimpled track that runs
All hollow through the wheat?
O that was where they hauled the guns
That smote King Philip's fleet.

See you our little mill that clacks,
So busy by the brook?
She has ground her corn and paid her tax
Ever since Domesday Book.

See you our stilly woods of oak,
And the dread ditch beside?
O that was where the Saxons broke
On the day that Harold died.

See you the windy levels spread
About the gates of Rye?
O that was where the Northmen fled,
When Alfred's ships came by.

See you our pastures wide and lone,
Where the red oxen browse?
O there was a City thronged and known
E're London boasted a house.

And see you, after rain, the trace
Of mound and ditch and wall?
O that was a Legion's camping-place,
When Caesar sailed from Gaul.

And see you marks that show and fade,
Like shadows on the Downs?
O they are the lines the Flint Men made,
To guard their wondrous towns.

Trackway and Camp and City lost,
Salt Marsh where now is corn;
Old Wars, old Peace, old Arts that cease,
And so was England born!

She is not any common Earth,
Water or wood or air,
But Merlin's Isle of Gramarye,
Where you and I will fare.

RUDYARD KIPLING

The New Jerusalem

And did those feet in ancient time
Walk upon England's mountains green?
And was the holy lamb of God
On England's pleasant pastures seen?

And did the Countenance Divine
Shine forth upon our clouded hills?
And was Jerusalem builded here
Among these dark Satanic Mills?

Bring me my bow of burning gold!
Bring me my arrows of desire!
Bring me my spear! O clouds, unfold!
Bring me my chariot of fire!

I will not cease from mental fight,
Nor shall my sword sleep in my hand,
Till we have built Jerusalem
In England's green and pleasant land.

WILLIAM BLAKE

Widdecombe Fair

'Tom Pearse, Tom Pearse, lend me your gray mare,'
(All along, down along, out along, lee),
'For I want for to go to Widdecombe Fair,
Wi' Bill Brewer, Jan Stewer, Peter Gurney, Peter Davy,
    Dan'l Whiddon, Harry Hawk,
And Uncle Tom Cobley and all.
Old Uncle Tom Cobley and all.'

'And when shall I see again my gray mare?'
(All along, down along, out along, lee),
'By Friday soon, or Saturday noon,
Wi' Bill Brewer, etc.'

Then Friday came and Saturday noon,
(All along, down along, out along, lee),
But Tom Pearse's old mare hath not trotted home.
Wi' Bill Brewer, etc.

So Tom Pearse he got up to the top o' the hill,
(All along, down along, out along, lee),
And he see'd his old mare down a-making her will —
Wi' Bill Brewer, etc.

Tom Pearce's old mare, her took sick and her died,
(All along, down along, out along, lee),
And Tom he sat down on a stone, and he cried —
Wi' Bill Brewer, etc.

But this isn't the end of this shocking affair,
(All along, down along, out along, lee),
Nor, though they be dead, of the horrid career
Of Bill Brewer, etc.

When the wind whistles cold on the moor of a night,
(All along, down along, out along, lee),
Tom Pearse's old mare doth appear, ghastly white,
Wi' Bill Brewer, etc.

And all the long night be heard skirling and groans
(All along, down along, out along, lee),
From Tom Pearse's old mare in her rattling bones,
And Bill Brewer, etc.

TRADITIONAL

Strawberry Fair

As I was going to Strawberry Fair,
Singing, singing, buttercups and daisies,
I met a maiden taking her ware,
Fol-de-dee.
Her eyes were blue, and golden her hair
As she went on to Strawberry Fair.
Ri-fol, Ri-fol, Fol-de-riddle-li-do,
Ri-fol, Ri-fol, Fol-de-riddle-dee.

'Kind sir, pray pick of my basket,' she said,
Singing, singing, buttercups and daisies,
'My cherries white or my roses red.'
Fol-de-dee.
'My strawberries sweet I can of them spare
As we go on to Strawberry Fair.'
Ri-fol, etc.

'Your cherries soon will be wasted away,'
Singing, singing, buttercups and daisies,
'Your roses wither and never stay,'
Fol-de-dee —
' 'Tis not to purchase such perishing ware
That I am tramping to Strawberry Fair.'
Ri-fol, etc.

'I want to purchase a generous heart,
Singing, singing, buttercups and daisies,
'A tongue that is neither nimble nor tart,'
Fol-de-dee,
'An honest mind, but such trifles are rare,
I doubt if they're found at Strawberry Fair.'
Ri-fol, etc.

'The price I offer, my sweet maid,'
Singing, singing, buttercups and daisies,
'A ring of gold on your finger displayed,'
Fol-de-dee!
'So come, make over to me your ware,
In church today at Strawberry Fair.'
Ri-fol, etc.

TRADITIONAL

One More River

The animals came in two by two,
Vive la compagnie.
The centipede with the kangaroo.
Vive la compagnie!
One more river, and that's the river of Jordan,
One more river, there's one more river to cross.

The animals came in three by three,
Vive la compagnie.
The elephant on the back of the flea.
Vive la compagnie!
One more river, etc.

The animals came in four by four,
Vive la compagnie.
The camel, he got stuck in the door.
Vive la compagnie!
One more river, etc.

The animals came in five by five,
Vive la compagnie.
Some were dead and some were alive.
Vive la compagnie!
One more river, etc.

The animals came in six by six,
Vive la compagnie.
The monkey, he was up to his tricks.
Vive la compagnie!
One more river, etc.

The animals came in seven by seven,
Vive la compagnie.
Some went to Hell, and some went to Heaven.
Vive la compagnie!
One more river, etc.

The animals came in eight by eight,
Vive la compagnie.
The worm was early the bird was late.
Vive la compagnie!
One more river, etc.

The animals came in nine by nine,
Vive la compagnie.
Some had water and some had wine.
Vive la compagnie!
One more river, etc.

The animals came in ten by ten,
Vive la compagnie.
If you want any more you must sing it again.
Vive la compagnie!
One more river, and that's the river of Jordan,
One more river, there's one more river to cross.

TRADITIONAL

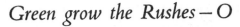

Green grow the Rushes — O

I'll sing you one — O!
Green grow the rushes — O.
What is your one — O?
One is one and all alone and ever more shall be so.

I'll sing you two — O!
Green grow the rushes — O.
What are your two — O?
Two, two, the lily white boys, clothed all in green — O.
One is one and all alone and ever more shall be so.

I'll sing you three — O!
Green grow the rushes — O.
What are your three — O?
Three, three, the rivals,
Two, two, the lily white boys, clothed all in green — O.
One is one and all alone and ever more shall be so.

I'll sing you four — O!
Green grow the rushes — O.
What are your four — O?
Four for the Gospel makers,
Three, three, the rivals,
Two, two, the lily white boys clothed all in green — O.
One is one and all alone and ever more shall be so.

I'll sing you five — O!
Green grow the rushes — O.
What are your five — O?
Five for the symbols at your door and four for the gospel
    makers,

Three, three, the rivals,
Two, two, the lily white boys clothed all in green — O.
One is one and all alone and ever more shall be so.

I'll sing you six — O!
Green grow the rushes — O.
What are your six — O?
Six for the six proud walkers,
Five for the symbols at your door and four for the Gospel
      makers,
Three, three, the rivals,
Two, two, the lily white boys, clothed all in green — O.
One is one and all alone and ever more shall be so.

I'll sing you seven — O!
Green grow the rushes — O.
What are your seven — O?
Seven for the seven stars in the sky and six for the six proud
      walkers,
Five for the symbols at your door and four for the Gospel
      makers,
Three, three, the rivals,
Two, two, the lily white boys, clothed all in green — O.
One is one and all alone and ever more shall be so.

I'll sing you eight — O!
Green grow the rushes — O.
What are your eight — O?
Eight for the April rainers,
Seven for the seven stars in the sky and six for the six proud
      walkers,

Five for the symbols at your door and four for the Gospel
    makers,
Three, three, the rivals,
Two, two, the lily white boys, clothed all in green — O.
One is one and all alone and ever more shall be so.

I'll sing you nine — O!
Green grow the rushes — O.
What are your nine — O?
Nine for the nine bright shiners,
Eight for the April rainers,
Seven for the seven stars in the sky and six for the six proud
    walkers,
Five for the symbols at your door and four for the Gospel
    makers,
Three, three, the rivals,
Two, two, the lily white boys clothed all in green — O.
One is one and all alone and ever more shall be so.

I'll sing you ten — O!
Green grow the rushes — O.
What are your ten — O?
Ten for the ten commandments,
Nine for the nine bright shiners,
Eight for the April rainers,
Seven for the seven stars in the sky and six for the six proud
    walkers,
Five for the symbols at your door and four for the Gospel
    makers,
Three, three, the rivals,
Two, two, the lily white boys, clothed all in green — O.
One is one and all alone and ever more shall be so.

I'll sing you eleven — O!
Green grow the rushes — O.
What are your eleven — O?
Eleven for the eleven went up to heaven and ten for the
    ten commandments,
Nine for the nine bright shiners,
Eight for the April rainers,
Seven for the seven stars in the sky and six for the six
    proud walkers,
Five for the symbols at your door and four for the Gospel
    makers,
Three, three, the rivals,
Two, two, the lily white boys clothed all in green — O.
One is one and all alone and ever more shall be so.

I'll sing you twelve — O!
Green grow the rushes — O.
What are your twelve — O?
Twelve for the twelve apostles,
Eleven for the eleven went up to heaven and ten for the
    ten commandments,
Nine for the nine bright shiners,
Eight for the April rainers,
Seven for the seven stars in the sky and six for the six
    proud walkers,
Five for the symbols at your door and four for the Gospel
    makers,
Three, three, the rivals,
Two, two, the lily white boys, clothed all in green — O.
One is one and all alone and ever more shall be so.

TRADITIONAL

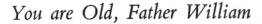

You are Old, Father William

'You are old, Father William;' the young man said,
'And your hair has become very white;
And yet you incessantly stand on your head —
Do you think, at your age, it is right?'

'In my youth,' Father William replied to his son,
'I feared it might injure the brain;
But, now that I'm perfectly sure I have none,
Why, I do it again and again.'

'You are old,' said the youth, 'as I mentioned before,
And have grown most uncommonly fat;
Yet you turned a back-somersault in at the door —
Pray, what is the reason of that?'

'In my youth,' said the sage, as he shook his grey locks,
'I kept all my limbs very supple
By the use of this ointment — one shilling the box —
Allow me to sell you a couple?'

'You are old,' said the youth, 'and your jaws are too weak
For anything tougher than suet,
Yet you finished the goose, with the bones and the beak —
Pray, how did you manage to do it?'

'In my youth,' said his Father, 'I took to the law,
And argued each case with my wife;
And the muscular strength which it gave to my jaw,
Has lasted the rest of my life.'

'You are old,' said the youth, 'one would hardly suppose,
That your eye was as steady as ever;
Yet you balanced an eel on the end of your nose —
What made you so awfully clever?'

'I have answered three questions, and that is enough,'
Said his Father: 'don't give yourself airs;
Do you think I can listen all day to such stuff?
Be off, or I'll kick you downstairs!'

LEWIS CARROLL

The Mad Gardener's Song

He thought he saw an Elephant
    That practised on a fife:
He looked again, and found it was
    A letter from his wife.
'At length I realise,' he said,
    'The bitterness of life!'

He thought he saw a Buffalo
    Upon the chimney-piece:
He looked again, and found it was
    His Sister's Husband's Niece.
'Unless you leave this house,' he said,
    'I'll send for the police!'

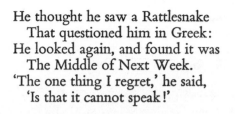

He thought he saw a Rattlesnake
    That questioned him in Greek:
He looked again, and found it was
    The Middle of Next Week.
'The one thing I regret,' he said,
    'Is that it cannot speak!'

He thought he saw a Banker's Clerk
    Descending from the bus:
He looked again, and found it was
    A Hippopotamus.
'If this should stay to dine,' he said,
    'There won't be much for us!'

He thought he saw a Kangaroo
    That worked a coffee-mill:
He looked again, and found it was
    A vegetable-pill.
'Were I to swallow this,' he said,
    'I should be very ill!'

He thought he saw a Coach-and-Four
    That stood beside his bed:
He looked again, and found it was
    A Bear without a Head.
'Poor thing,' he said, 'poor silly thing!
    It's waiting to be fed!'

LEWIS CARROLL

Brother and Sister

'Sister, sister, go to bed,
Go and rest your weary head,'
This the prudent brother said.

'Do you want a battered hide
Or scratches to your face applied?'
Thus the sister calm replied.

'Sister! Do not rouse my wrath,
I'd make you into mutton broth
As easily as kill a moth.'

The sister raised her beaming eye,
And looked on him indignantly,
And sternly answered, 'Only try!'

Off to the cook he quickly ran,
'Dear cook, pray lend a frying pan
To me, as quickly as you can.'

'And wherefore should I give it you?'
'The reason, cook, is plain to view,
I wish to make an Irish stew.'

'What meat is in that stew to go?'
'My sister be the contents.' 'Oh!'
'Will you lend the pan, cook?' 'NO!'

Moral: 'Never stew your sister.'

LEWIS CARROLL

Sir Smasham Uppe

Good afternoon, Sir Smasham Uppe!
We're having tea: do take a cup!
Sugar and milk? Now let me see —
Two lumps, I think? ... Good gracious me!
The silly thing slipped off your knee!
Pray don't apologize, old chap;
A very trivial mishap!
So clumsy of you? How absurd!
My dear Sir Smasham, not a word!
Now do sit down and have another,
And tell us all about your brother —
You know, the one who broke his head.
Is the poor fellow still in bed? —
A chair — allow me, sir! ... Great Scott!
That *was* a nasty smash! Eh, what?
Oh, not at all: the chair was old —
Queen Anne, or so we have been told.
We've got at least a dozen more:
Just leave the pieces on the floor.
I want you to admire our view:
Come nearer to the window, do;
And look how beautiful ... Tut, tut!
You didn't see that it was shut?
I hope you are not badly cut!
Not hurt? A fortunate escape!
Amazing! Not a single scrape!
And now, if you have finished tea,
I fancy you might like to see
A little thing or two I've got.

That china plate? Yes, worth a lot:
A beauty too . . . Ah, there it goes!
I trust it didn't hurt your toes?
Your elbow brushed it off the shelf?
Of course: I've done the same myself.
And now, my dear Sir Smasham — Oh,
You surely don't intend to go?
You *must* be off? Well, come again.
So glad you're fond of porcelain!

E. V. RIEU

The Old Fellow of Tring

There was an old fellow of Tring
Who, when somebody asked him to sing,
Replied, 'Ain't it odd?
I can never tell 'God
Save the Weasel' from 'Pop goes the King'.'

TRADITIONAL

The Young Man of Japan

There was a young man of Japan
Whose limericks never would scan.
When told it was so,
He replied, 'Yes, I know,
But I always try to get as many words into the last line as ever
I possibly can.'

TRADITIONAL

Matilda

Who told lies, and was burned to death.

Matilda told such dreadful lies,
It made one gasp and stretch one's eyes;
Her Aunt, who from her Earliest Youth,
Had kept a strict regard for truth,
Attempted to believe Matilda:
The effort very nearly killed her,
And would have done so, had not she
Discovered this Infirmity.
For once, towards the close of day
Matilda, growing tired of play
And finding she was left alone,
Went tiptoe to the Telephone,
And summoned the immediate Aid
Of London's Noble Fire-Brigade.
Within an hour the gallant band
Were pouring in on every hand,
From Putney, Hackney, Downs and Bow.
With courage high and hearts a-glow,
They galloped, roaring through the town,
'Matilda's House is burning down!'
Inspired by British Cheers and Loud
Proceeding from the frenzied crowd,
They ran their ladders through a score
Of windows on the Bathroom Floor;
And took peculiar pains to souse
The Pictures up and down the House,
Until Matilda's Aunt succeeded
In showing them they were not needed;

And even then she had to pay
To get the Men to go away!
It happened that a few weeks later
Her Aunt was off to the Theatre
To see that interesting play
'The second Mrs Tanqueray.'
She had refused to take her Niece
To hear that entertaining Piece:
A Deprivation just and wise
To punish her for telling lies.
That night a fire did break out —
You should have heard Matilda shout!
You should have heard her scream and bawl!
And throw the window up and call
To people passing in the street —
(The rapidly increasing Heat
Encouraging her to obtain
Their confidence) — but all in vain!
For every time she shouted 'Fire!'
They only answered 'Little Liar!'
And therefore when her Aunt returned,
Matilda, and the House, were burned.

HILAIRE BELLOC

Tartary

If I were Lord of Tartary,
Myself, and me alone,
My bed should be of ivory,
Of beaten gold my throne;
And in my court should peacocks flaunt,
And in my forests tigers haunt,
And in my pools great fishes slant
Their fins athwart the sun.

If I were Lord of Tartary,
Trumpeters every day
To all my meals should summon me,
And in my courtyards bray;
And in the evenings lamps should shine,
Yellow as honey, red as wine,
While harp, and flute and mandoline
Made music sweet and gay.

If I were Lord of Tartary,
I'd wear a robe of beads,
White, and gold, and green they'd be —
And small and thick as seeds;
And ere should dawn the morning star,
I'd don my robe and scimitar,
And zebras seven should draw my car
Through Tartary's dark glades.

Lord of the fruits of Tartary,
Her rivers silver-pale!
Lord of the hills of Tartary,
Glen, thicket, wood, and dale!
Her flashing stars, her scented breeze,
Her trembling lakes, like foamless seas,
Her bird-delighting citron-trees
In every purple vale!

WALTER DE LA MARE

Ulysses

Come, my friends,
'Tis not too late to seek a newer world.
Push off, and sitting well in order smite
The sounding furrows; for my purpose holds
To sail beyond the sunset, and the baths
Of all the western stars, until I die.
It may be that the gulfs will wash us down;
It may be we shall touch the Happy Isles,
And see the great Achilles whom we knew.

ALFRED, LORD TENNYSON
from 'Ulysses'

Wander - thirst

Beyond the East the sunrise, beyond the West the sea,
And East and West the wander-thirst that will not let me be;
It works in me like madness dear, to bid me say good-bye;
For the seas call, and the stars call, and oh! the call of the sky!

I know not where the white road runs, nor what the blue hills
    are;
But a man can have the sun for friend and for his guide a star;
And there is no end of voyaging, when once the voice is heard,
For the river calls and the road calls, and oh! the call of a bird!

Yonder the long horizon lies, and there by night and day
The old ships draw to home again, the young ships sail away;
And come I may, but go I must and, if men ask you why,
You may put the blame on the stars and the sun and the
    white road and the sky.

GERALD GOULD

Space Travellers

There was a witch, hump-backed and hooded,
Lived by herself in a burnt-out tree.
When storm winds shrieked and the moon was buried
And the dark of the forest was black as black,
She rose in the air like a rocket at sea,
     Riding the wind,
     Riding the night,
Riding the tempest to the moon and back.

There may be a man with a hump of silver,
Telescope eyes and a Telephone ear,
Dials to twist and knobs to twiddle,
Waiting for a night when skies are clear,
To shoot from the scaffold with a blazing track,
     Riding the dark,
     Riding the cold,
Riding the silence to the moon and back.

JAMES NIMMO

Eldorado

Gaily bedight,
A gallant knight,
In sunshine and in shadow,
Had journeyed long,
Singing a song,
In search of Eldorado.

But he grew old,
This knight so bold,
And o'er his heart a shadow
Fell as he found
No spot of ground
That looked like Eldorado.

And, as his strength
Failed him at length,
He met a pilgrim shadow:
'Shadow,' said he,
'Where can it be,
The land of Eldorado?'

'Over the Mountains
Of the Moon,
Down the Valley of the Shadow,
Ride, boldly ride,'
The shade replied,
'If you seek for Eldorado.'

EDGAR ALLAN POE